# The Joy of Show Music

**Arranged by Cyril Ornadel.**

**Yorktown Music Press / Music Sales Limited**
London / New York / Paris / Sydney / Copenhagen / Madrid

5-95

*Exclusive Distributors:*
Music Sales Limited
8/9 Frith Street, London W1V 5TZ, England.
Music Sales Pty Limited
120 Rothschild Avenue, Rosebery, NSW 2018, Australia.

This book © Copyright 1993 by
Yorktown Music Press/Music Sales Limited
Order No.AM90199
ISBN 0-7119-3252-2

Cover illustration by Gillian Martin
Compiled by Peter Evans
Music arranged by Cyril Ornadel
Music processed by Barnes Music Engraving

Music Sales' complete catalogue lists thousands of titles and is
free from your local music shop, or direct from Music Sales Limited.
Please send a cheque/postal order for £1.50 for postage to:
Music Sales Limited, Newmarket Road, Bury St. Edmunds, Suffolk IP33 3YB.

Your Guarantee of Quality

As publishers, we strive to produce every book to the highest commercial standards.

The music has been freshly engraved and the book has been carefully designed to
minimise awkward page turns and to make playing from it a real pleasure.

Particular care has been given to specifying acid-free, neutral-sized paper
which has not been chlorine bleached but produced with special regard for the environment.
Throughout, the printing and binding have been planned to ensure a sturdy,
attractive publication which should give years of enjoyment.

If your copy fails to meet our high standards, please inform us and we will gladly replace it.

Printed in the United Kingdom by
J.B. Offset Printers (Marks Tey) Limited, Marks Tey, Essex.

# Guys And Dolls
# A Woman In Love

Words and Music by Frank Loesser.

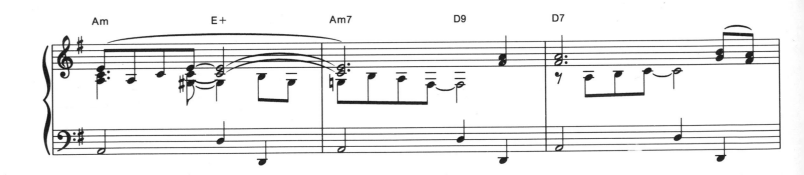

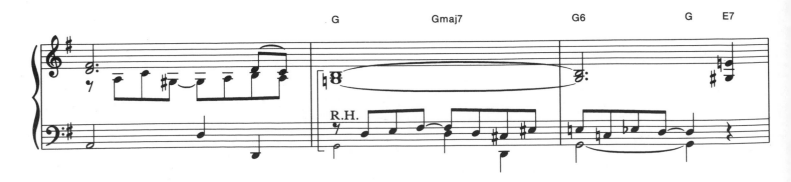

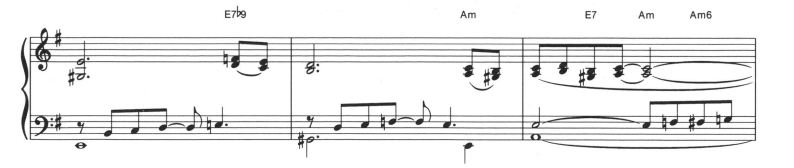

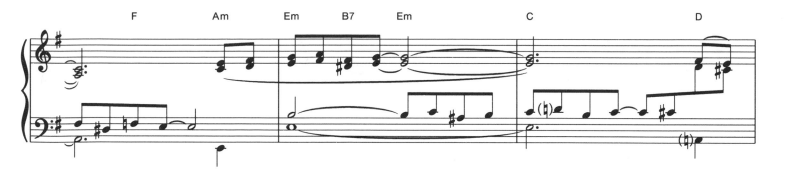

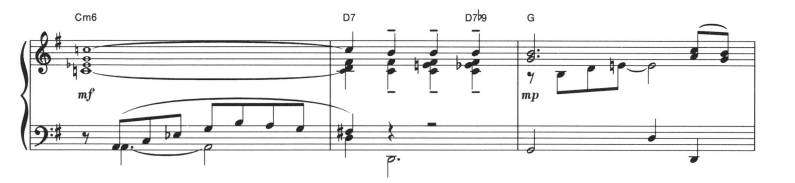

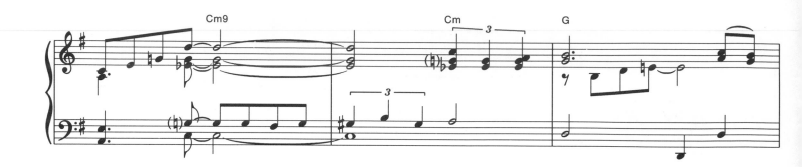

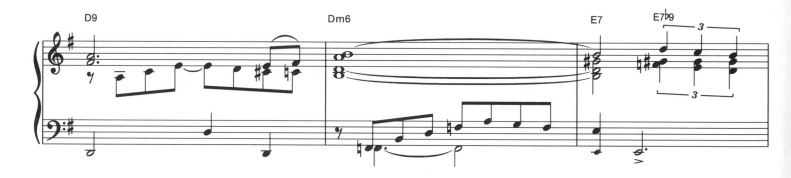

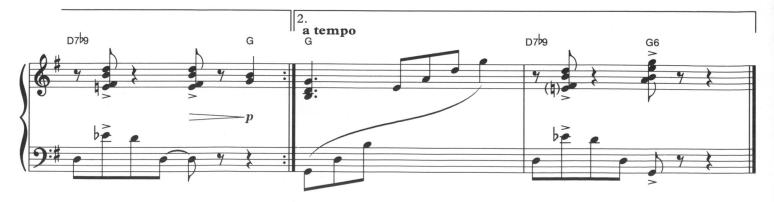

6

# Bubbling Brown Sugar
# Ain't Misbehavin'

Words by Andy Razaf. Music by Thomas Waller & Harry Brooks.

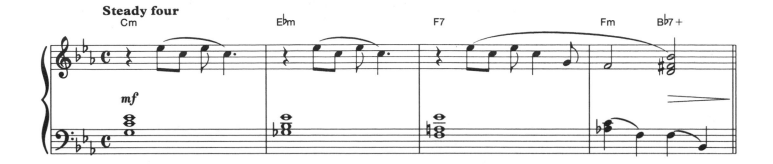

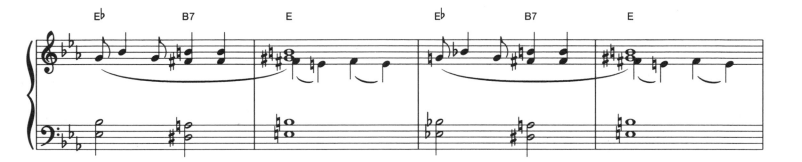

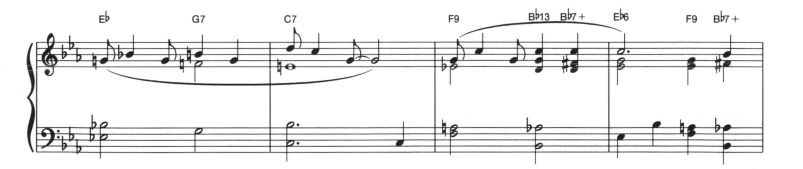

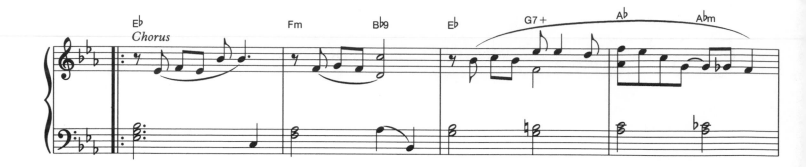

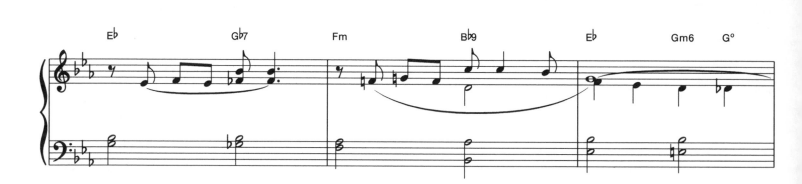

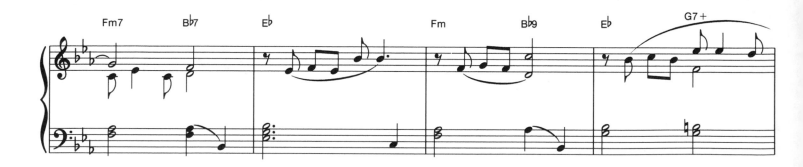

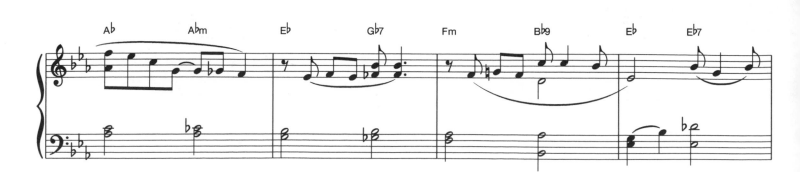

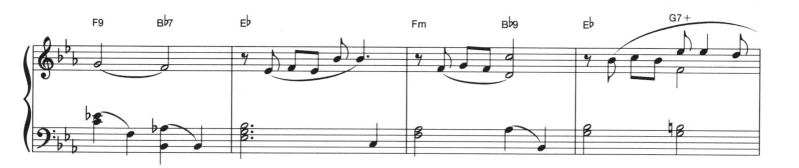

# Evita
# Another Suitcase In Another Hall

Music by Andrew Lloyd Webber. Lyrics by Tim Rice.

**Slowly (8 beat feel)**

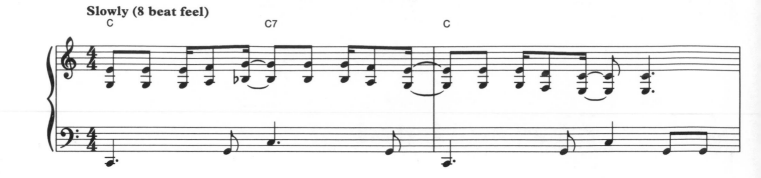

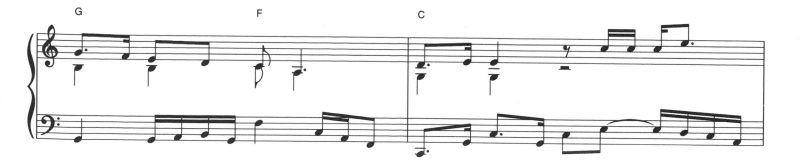

11

# Gentlemen Prefer Blondes
# Bye Bye Baby

Words by Leo Robin. Music by Jule Styne.

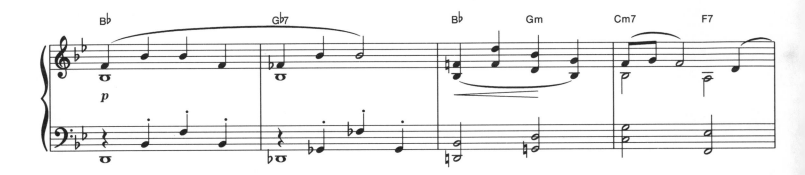

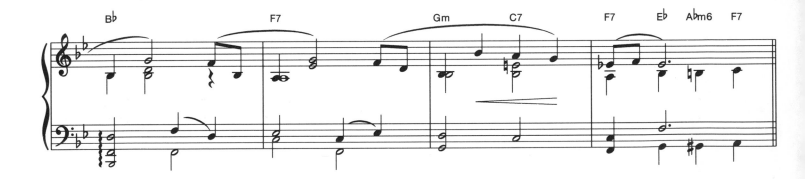

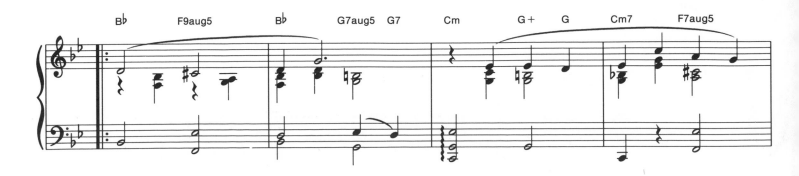

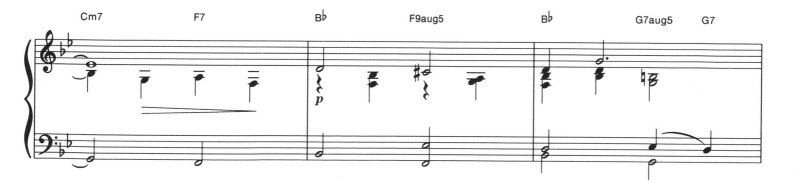

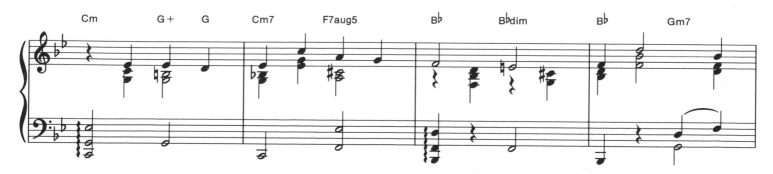

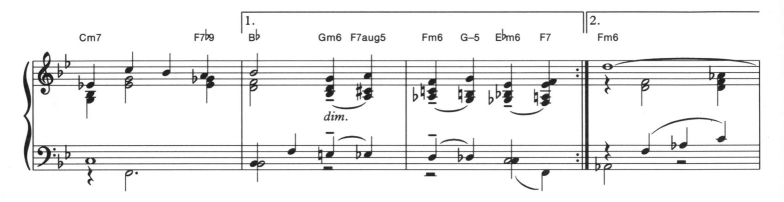

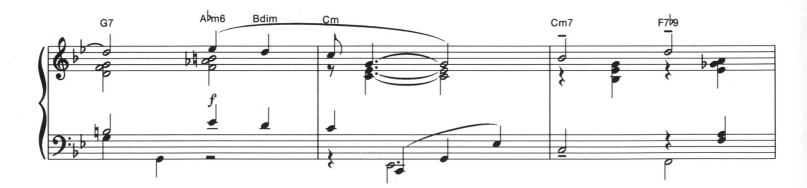

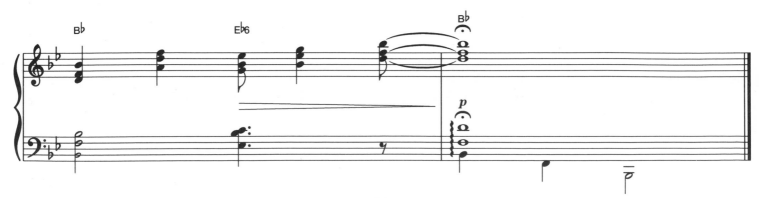

# Five Guys Named Moe
# Choo Choo Ch'Boogie

Words and Music by Vaughn Horton, Denver Darling & Milt Gabler.

**Fast boogie**

# Godspell
# Day By Day

Words and Music by Stephen Schwartz.

**Easy waltz feel**

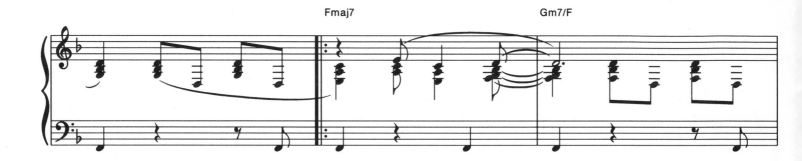

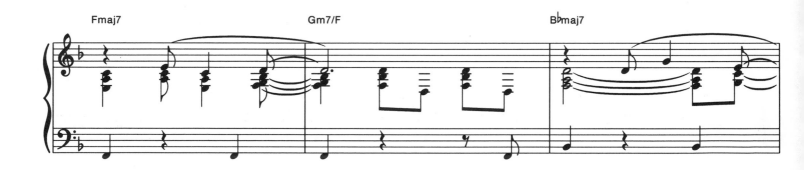

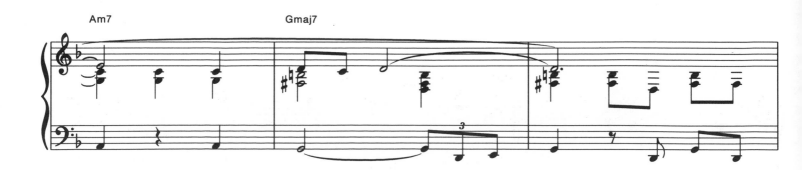

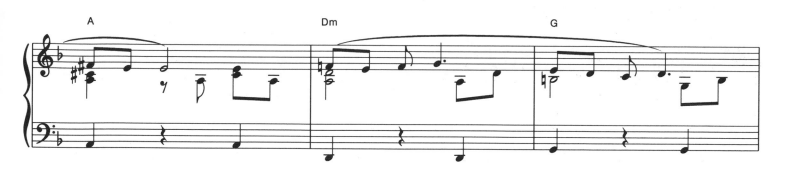

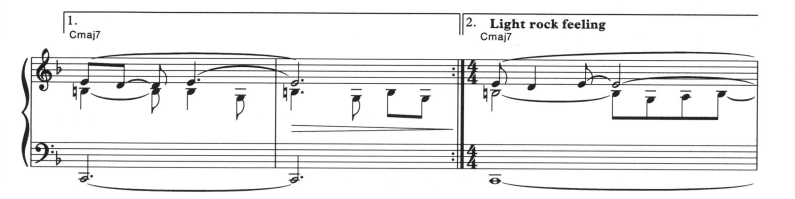

**1.** Cmaj7

**2. Light rock feeling** Cmaj7

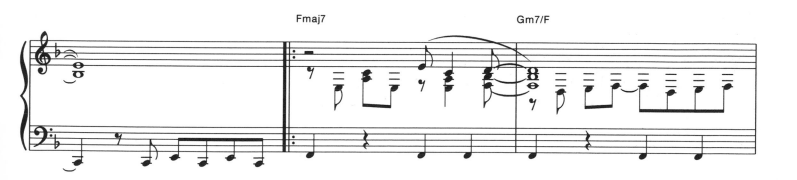

Fmaj7  Gm7/F

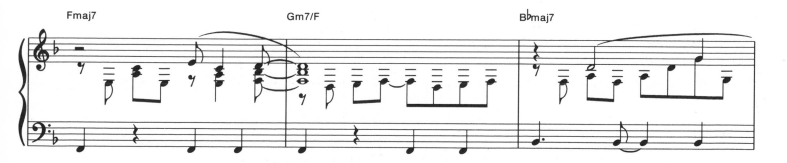

Fmaj7  Gm7/F  B♭maj7

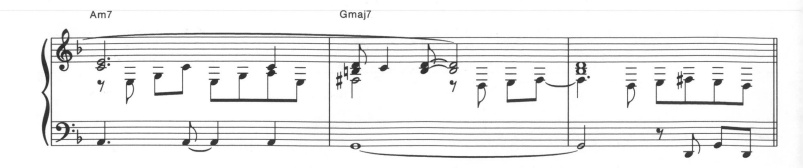

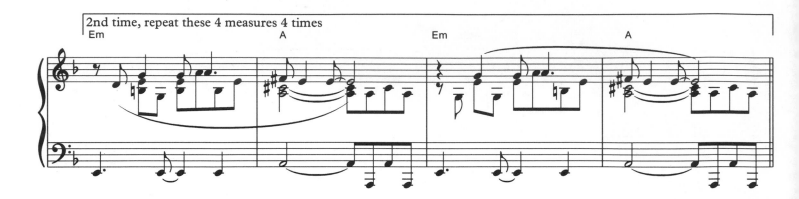

2nd time, repeat these 4 measures 4 times

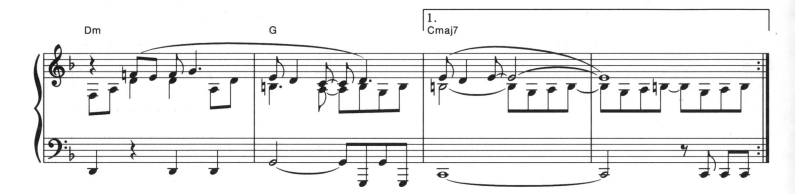

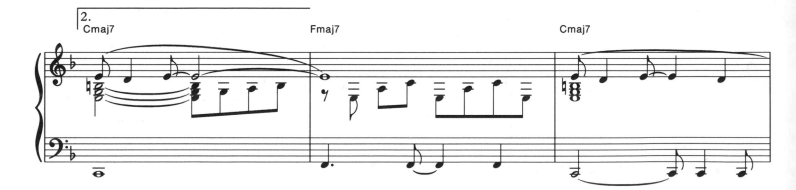

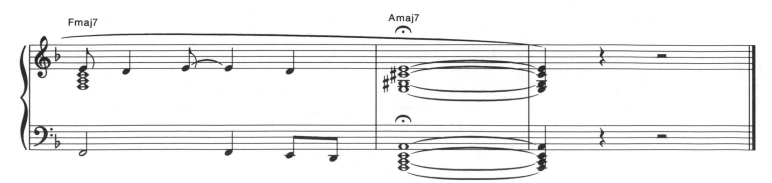

20

# Five Guys Named Moe
# Don't Let The Sun Catch You Crying

Words and Music by Joe Greene.

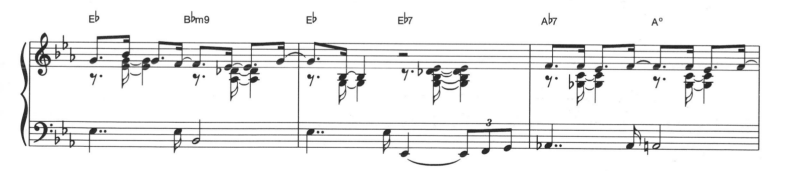

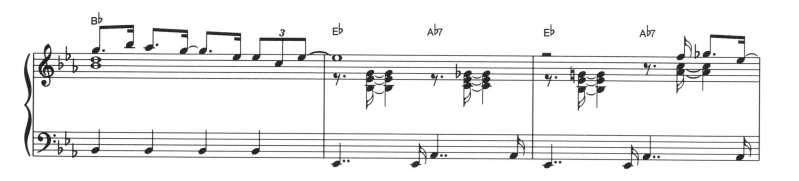

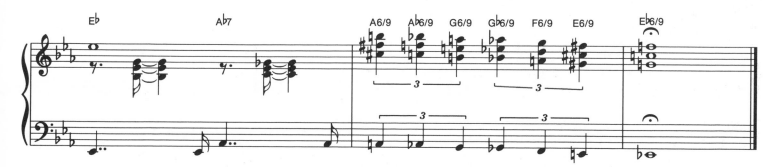

# Les Misérables
# I Dreamed A Dream

Music by Claude-Michel Schonberg. Lyrics by Herbert Kretzmer.
Original text by Alain Boublil & Jean-Marc Natel.

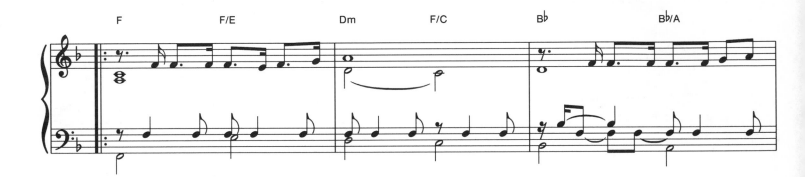

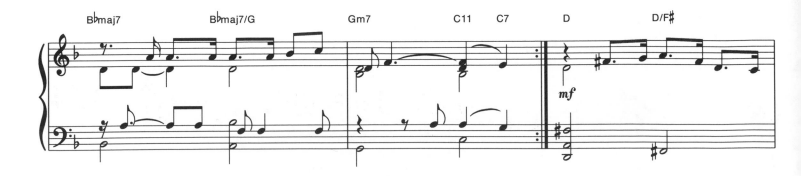

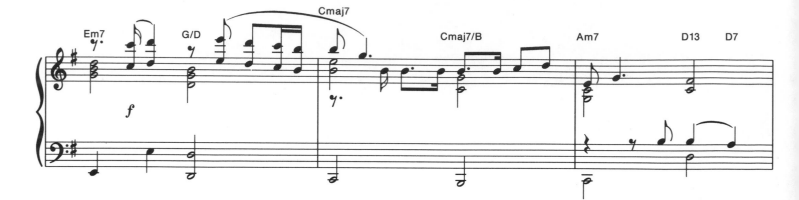

# Chess
# I Know Him So Well

*Words and Music by Benny Andersson, Tim Rice & Bjorn Ulvaeus.*

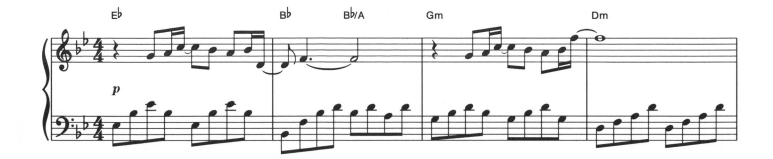

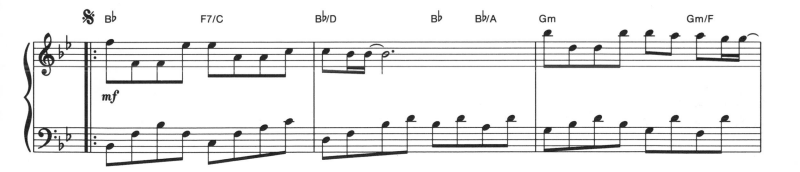

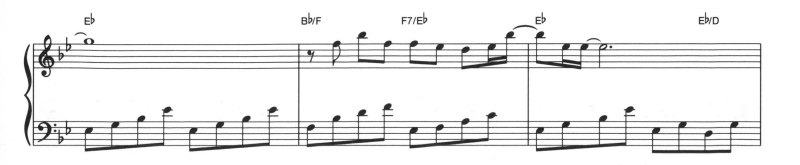

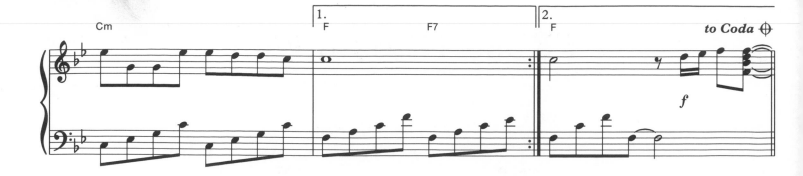

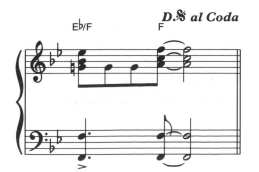

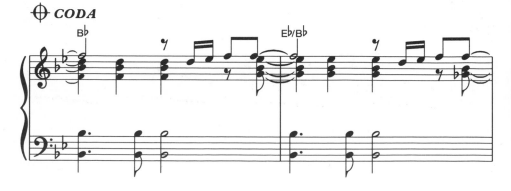

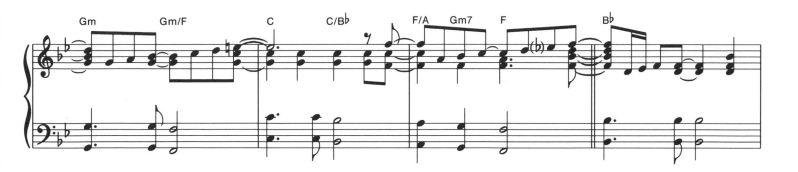

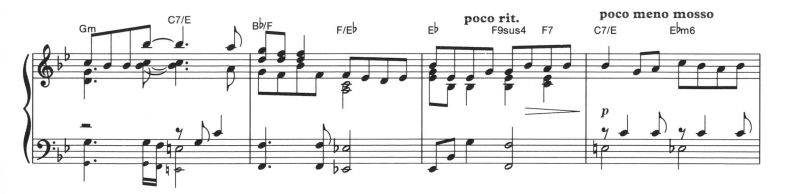

# I Feel Pretty

Music by Leonard Bernstein. Lyrics by Stephen Sondheim.

Brightly (alla Spagnola)

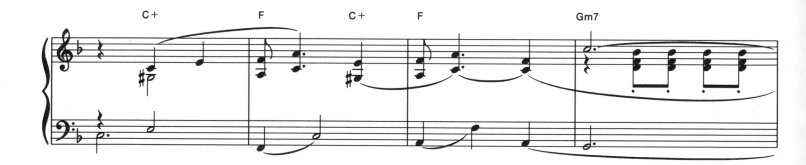

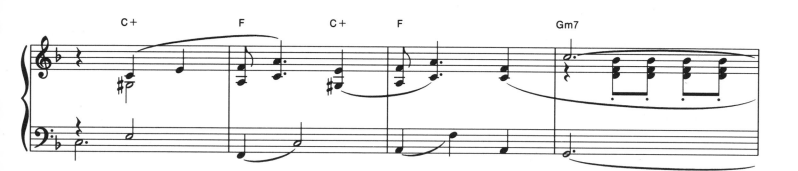

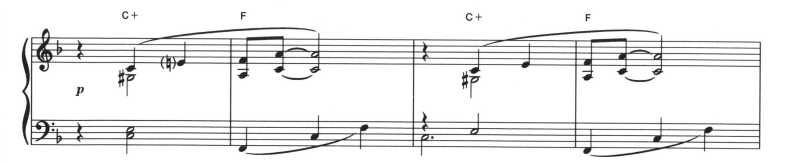

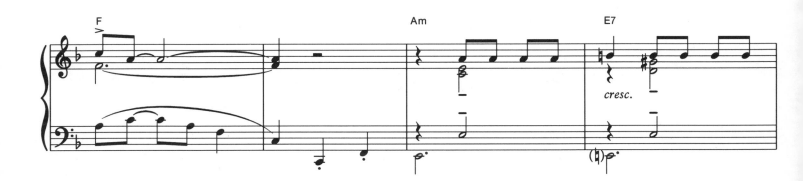

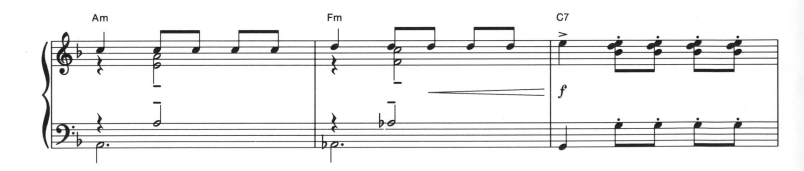

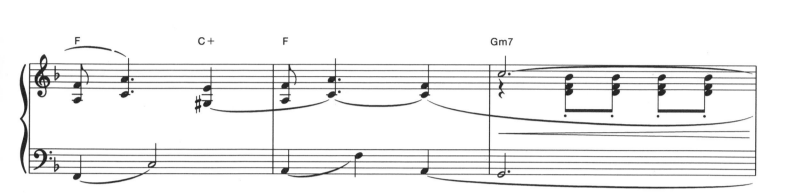

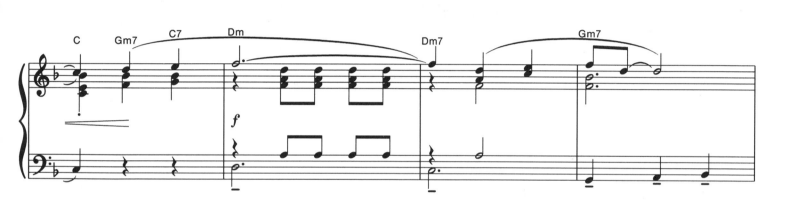

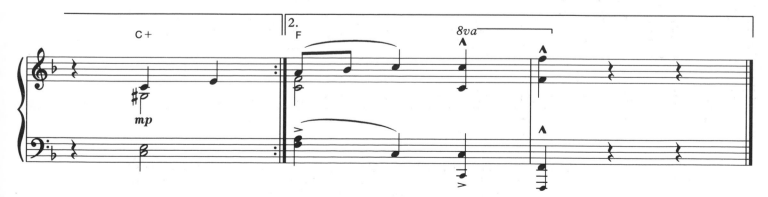

# Fiddler On The Roof
# If I Were A Rich Man

Words by Sheldon Harnick. Music by Jerry Bock.

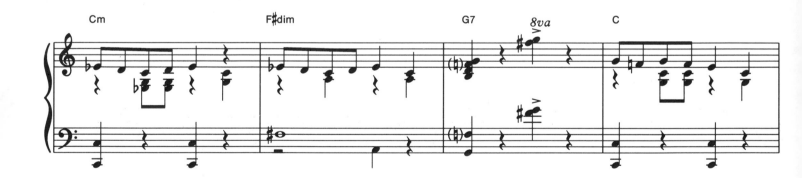

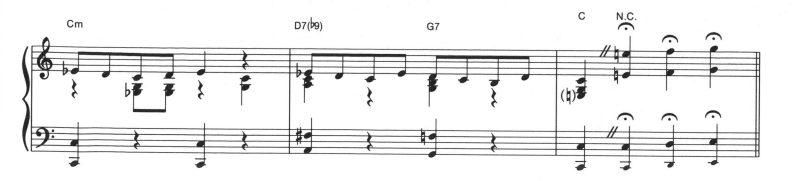

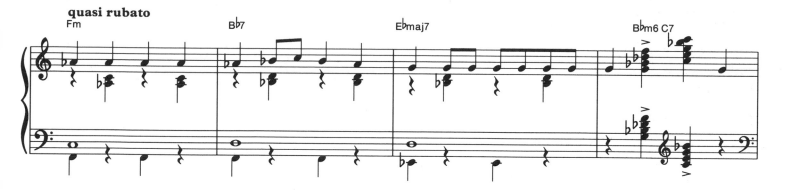

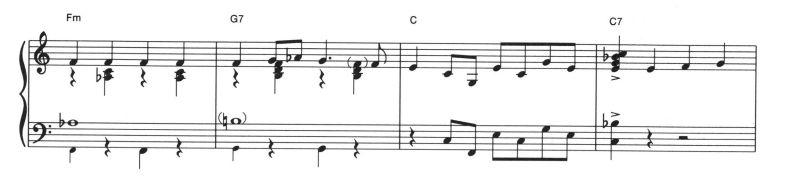

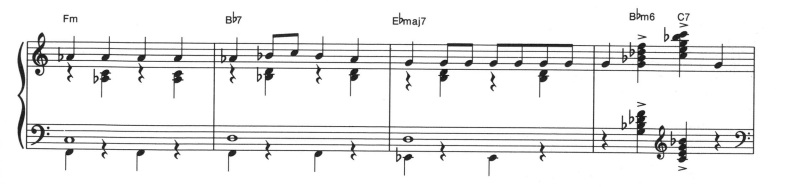

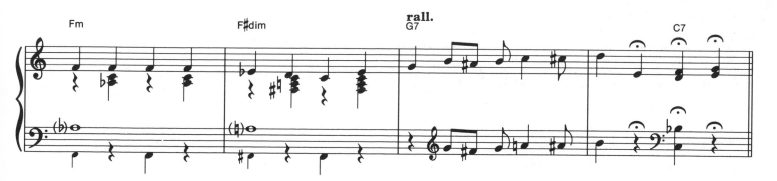

reflective, lyrical, soft

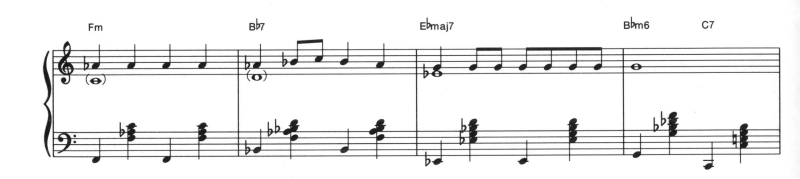

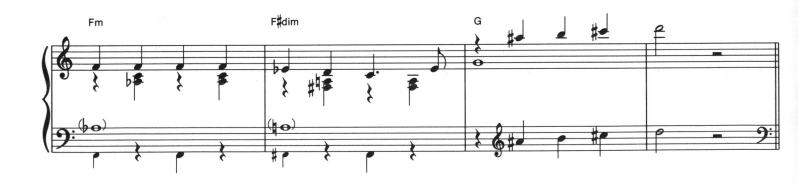

tempo primo

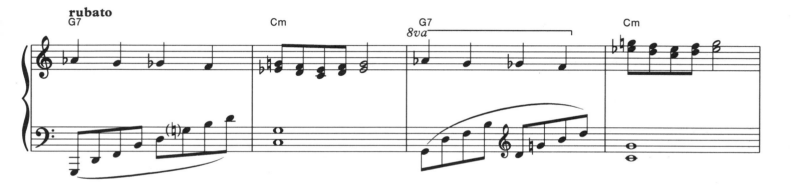

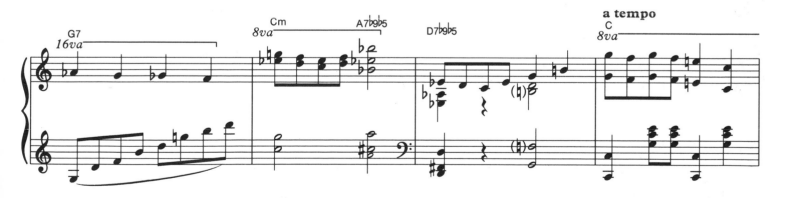

# Sweet Charity
# If My Friends Could See Me Now

Words by Dorothy Fields. Music by Cy Coleman.

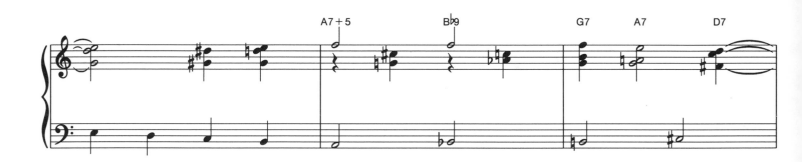

# Me And My Girl
# Lambeth Walk

Music by Noel Gay. Words by Douglas Furber & Arthur Rose.

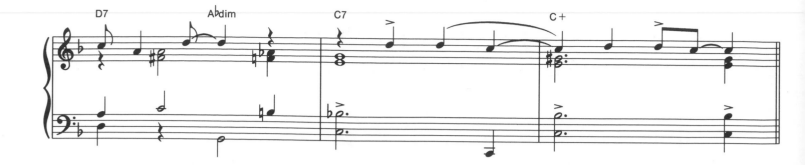

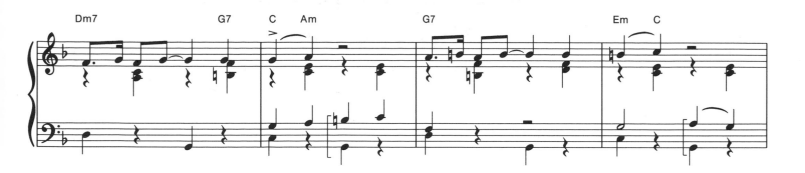

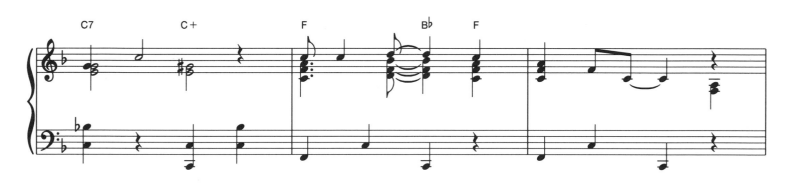

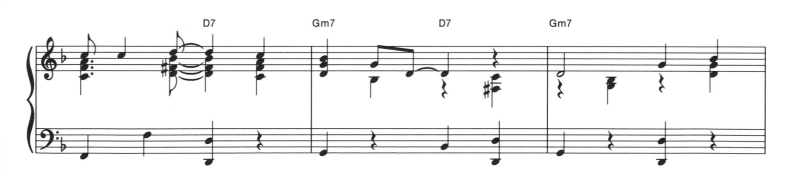

43

# Jesus Christ Superstar
# Superstar

Music by Andrew Lloyd Webber. Lyrics by Tim Rice.

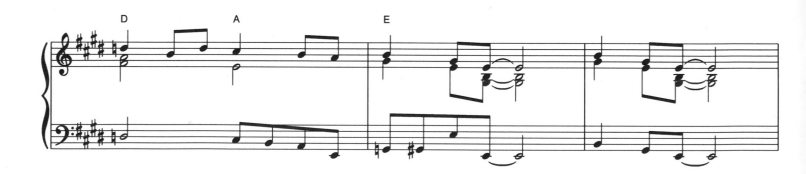

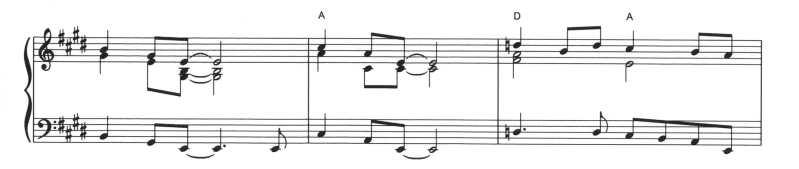

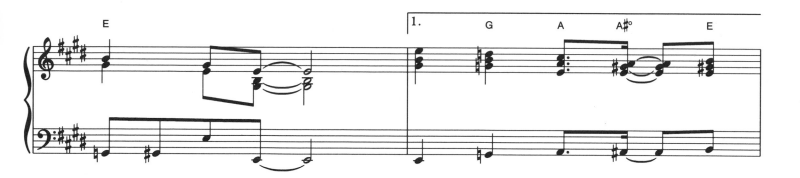

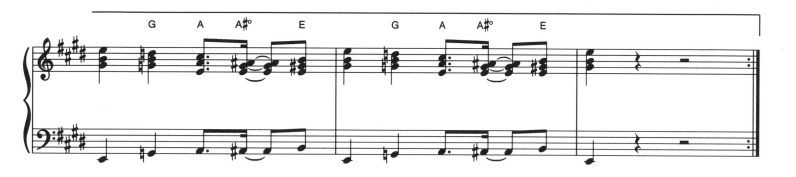

# The Music Man
# Seventy Six Trombones

Words and Music by Meredith Willson.

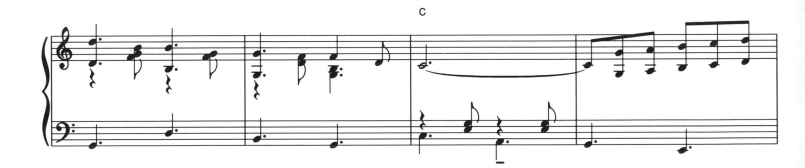

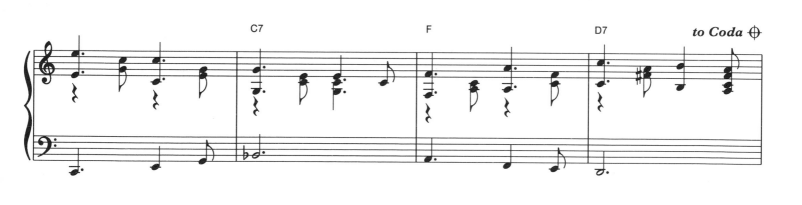

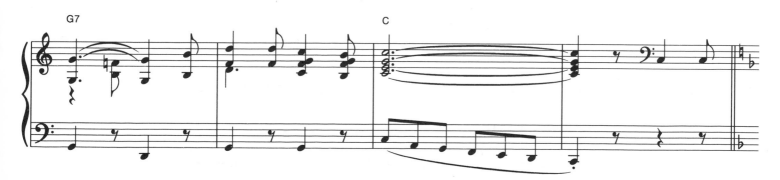

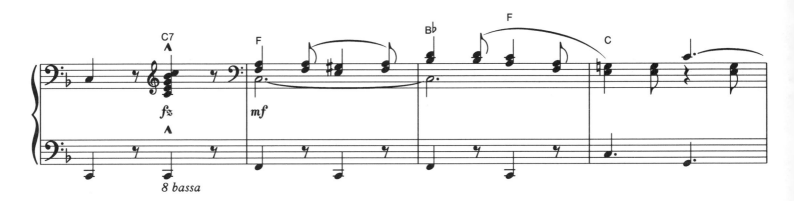

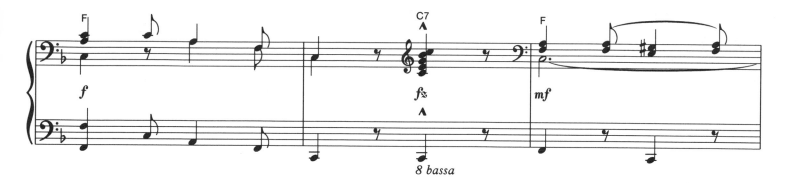

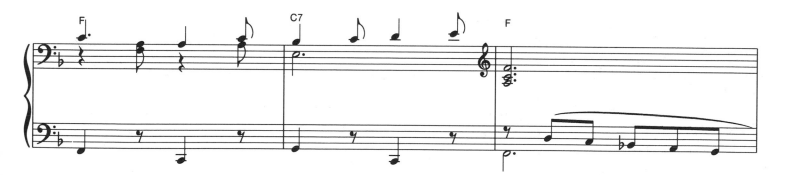

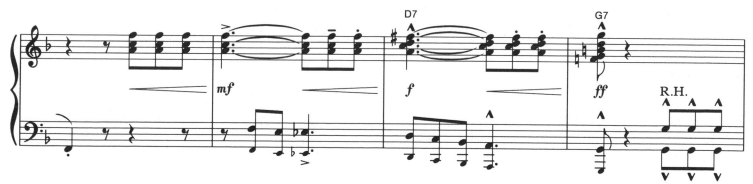

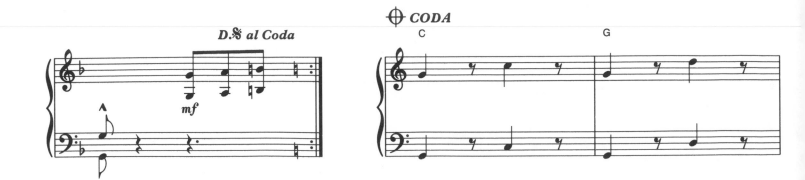

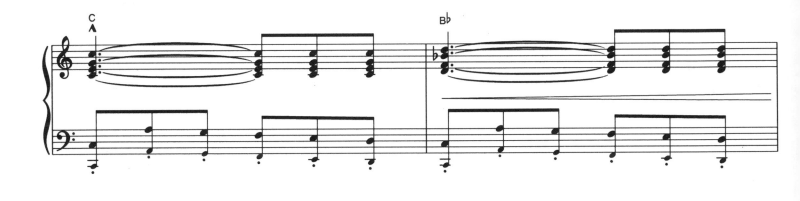

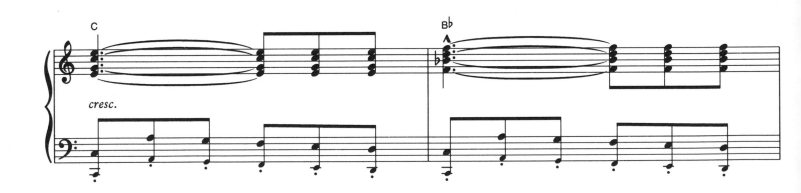

52

# Kismet
# Stranger In Paradise

Words and Music by Robert Wright & George Forrest.

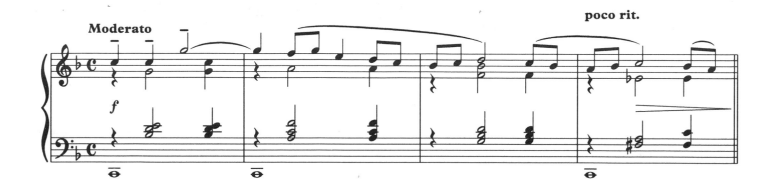

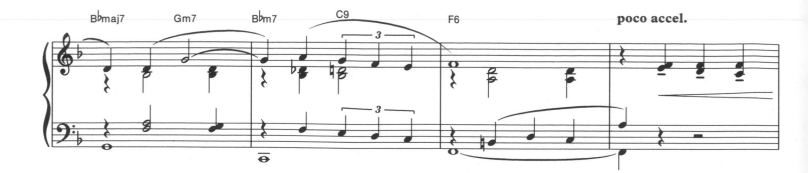

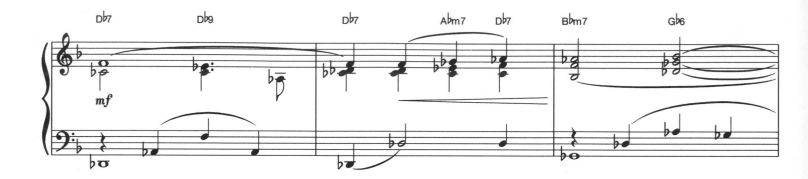

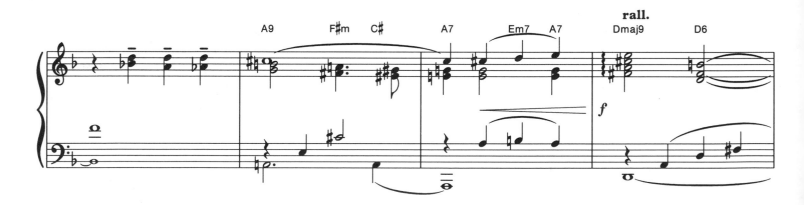

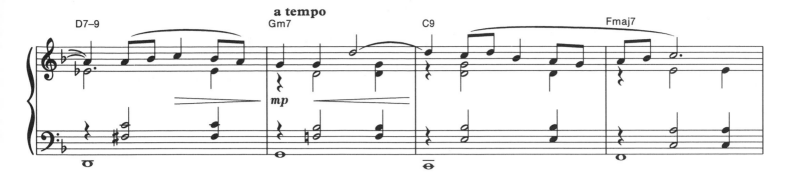

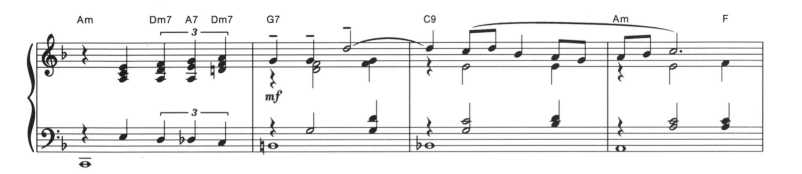

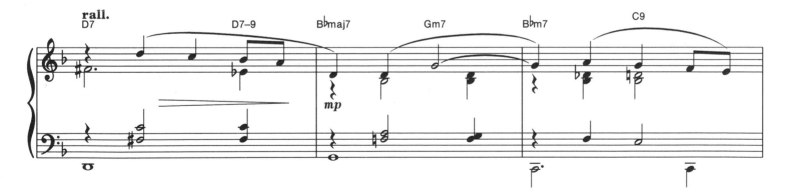

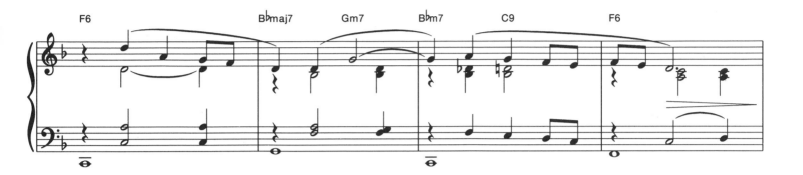

# Tell Me On A Sunday

Words by Don Black. Music by Andrew Lloyd Webber.

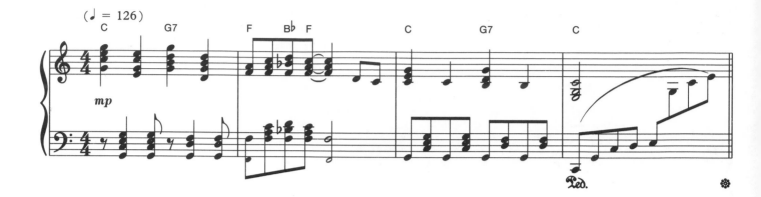

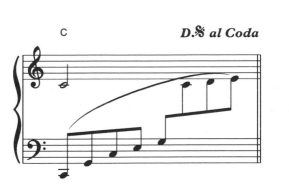

57

# Annie
# Tomorrow

Music by Charles Strouse. Words by Martin Charnin.

**Moderately**

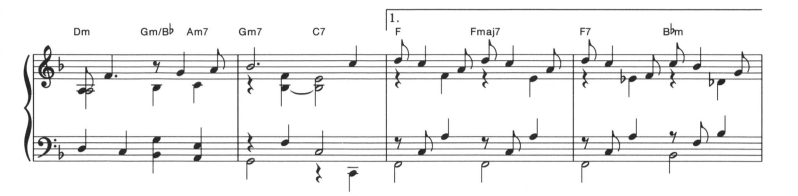

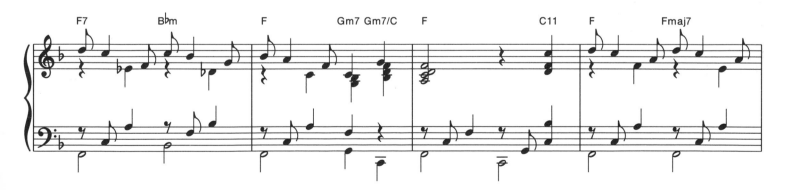

# Oliver

# Where Is Love

*Words and Music by Lionel Bart.*

**Slowly, but rhythmically**

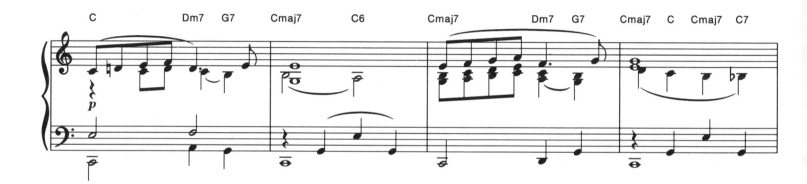

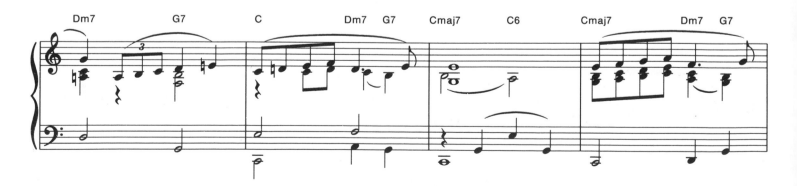

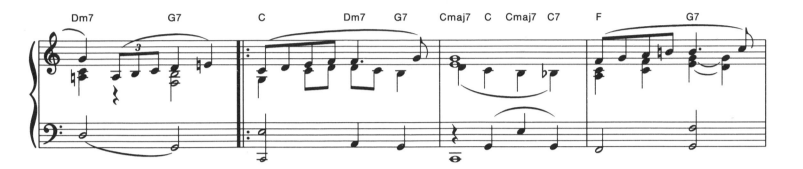

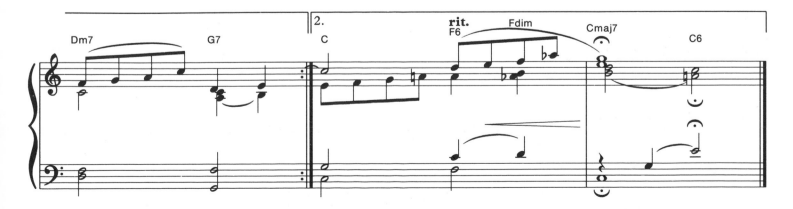

# Underneath The Arches

Words and Music by Bud Flanagan.

**Slow foxtrot**

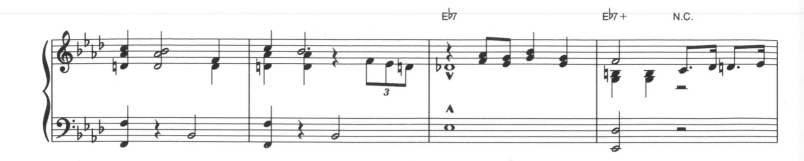